Contents

Years and leap years

Learn

There are **365 days** in a **year**.

Every fourth year is called a **leap year**. A leap year has 366 days. February has the extra day because that is the shortest month.

Here is a rhyme to help you remember how many days are in each month:

> 30 days have September,
> April, June and November.
> All the rest have 31,
> Except for February alone,
> Which has 28 days clear
> And 29 in each leap year.

1 Write how many days there are in each month of the year.

Month	Number of days
January	
February	or in a leap year
March	
April	
May	
June	
July	
August	
September	
October	
November	
December	

Did you know?

If your birthday is on 29th February and you were born during a leap year, then technically you only get a birthday once every four years!

Years, decades and centuries

earn

There are **52 weeks** in a **year**.

There are **10 years** in a **decade**.

There are **100 years** in a **century**.

1 Tick the correct amount of time for each picture.

How long does it take for a toddler to become a teenager?

	a year
	a decade
	a century

How long does it take for a tree to grow from a seed into a large tree?

	a year
	a decade
	a century

How long does it take to build a house?

	a year
	a decade
	a century

2 Answer these questions.

How many years are there in 2 decades? _____ years

How many years are there in 5 decades? _____ years

How many years are there in 3 centuries? _____ years

How many decades are there in a century? _____ decades

Did you know?

The Summer Olympic Games are held during leap years. In Ancient Greece the period of four years between each Olympics was called an Olympiad.

Calendars

You can use a **calendar** to keep track of the **days**, **weeks** and **months** in a **year**.

1 Look at the calendar page for February and answer the questions below.

What day of the week is 1st February? _____

What day of the week was the last day of January? _____

How many Thursdays are there in this month? _____

How many weekends are there in this month? _____

What day of the week is the last day of February? _____

What day of the week will 1st March be? _____

Is this a leap year? Explain how you know. _____

_____

Did you know?

January was named after the Roman god Janus, who was the god of endings and beginnings. He had one face at the front of his head and another face at the back, so he could look forwards and backwards. In January, people look forward to the new year and back at the old one, just like Janus.

Calendars

(2) Look at this calendar page for June and answer the questions below.

Adam's birthday is on 9th June.
On what day of the week is his birthday? _____

Nadia goes to tennis lessons every Monday.
How many lessons will she have in June? _____

Adam goes to a dance class every Friday.
How many classes will he have in June? _____

Adam is visiting his grandmother on the second
Saturday of the month. What date is that? _____

Nadia's birthday is on 1st July.
What day of the week will that be? _____

If today is 17th June, how many weeks does
Nadia have to wait until it is her birthday? _____

Did you know?

The calendar above is called the Gregorian calendar. Different people around
the world use different calendars. In the Chinese calendar each year is a different
animal. You could be born in the Year of the Rooster or Year of the Rat!

Minutes past

1 What time is it?

It is _____ minutes past _____.

It is _____ minutes past _____.

It is _____.

It is _____.

2 Draw lines to match each clock to the correct time.

| 25 minutes past 2 | quarter past 11 | 5 minutes past 5 |

Schofield & Sims Telling the Time 3

Minutes to

1 What time is it?

It is _____ minutes to _____ .

It is _____ minutes to _____ .

It is _____ .

It is _____ .

2 Draw the hands on these clocks to show the correct time.

25 minutes to 8

10 minutes to 2

5 minutes to 11

Digital time

This is an **analogue** clock.

This is a **digital** clock.

These clocks show the same time.

It is 25 minutes past 3. In digital time this is written as **3:25**.

Remember, in digital time you write the **hour** first and then the minutes past.

These clocks show the same time.

It is 10 minutes to 8. In digital time this is written as **7:50**.

Remember, in digital time you write the **hour** first and then the minutes past.

1 Read these digital clocks and write the times below.

It is _____ minutes past _____ .

It is _____ minutes past _____ .

It is _____ minutes to _____ .

Digital time

2 Draw lines to match the clocks that show the same time.

3 Draw the hands on these clocks to show the correct time.

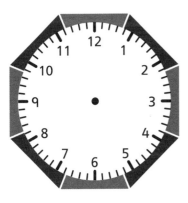 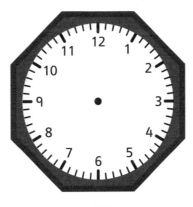 

12:20   1:40   6:55

4 Write the numbers on these digital clocks to show the correct time.

quarter past 8   25 minutes to 11   10 minutes to 10

Did you know?

Most phones, computers, cars and radios have digital clocks. Some devices use the Internet to make sure that the time is correct.

Tell the time to the minute past

It helps to count in 5s when you tell the time. This is because you can count 5 minutes for each number on the clock that the **big hand** has passed.

Sometimes you need to tell the time exactly. If the **big hand** is <u>between</u> numbers, you can count the **1 minute marks** around the clock face. It still helps to count mainly in 5s.

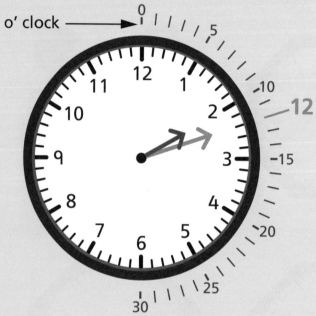

The **big hand** has passed **10 minutes past** but it hasn't yet got to **15 minutes past**. It is **12 minutes past** 2. In digital time this is **2:12**.

---

(1) Count the minute marks from o'clock to the big hand. Then write the time below.

It is _____ minutes past _____.

Tell the time to the minute past

2 What time is it?

It is _____ minutes past _____.

It is _____ : _____.

It is _____ minutes past _____.

It is _____ : _____.

It is _____.

It is _____ : _____.

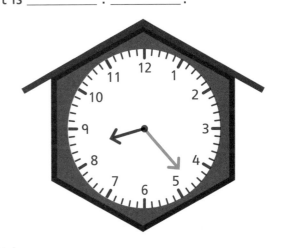

It is _____.

It is _____ : _____.

3 Tick the time that is the odd one out.

 ☐

 ☐

 ☐

4 Tick the time that is the odd one out.

 ☐

 ☐

 ☐

Tell the time to the minute to

If the big hand is between two numbers on the left-hand side of the clock, you count the **1 minute marks** back from o'clock. It still helps to count mainly in 5s.

The big hand has more than 20 minutes to go to the next o'clock, but less than 25 minutes.

It is 23 minutes to 3. In digital time this is 2:37.

Remember, there are **60 minutes** in an hour. So if it is 37 minutes past 2, there are 23 minutes to go until 3 o'clock.

1 Count the minute marks from o'clock to the big hand. Then write the time below.

It is _____ minutes to _____.

Tell the time to the minute to

(2) What time is it?

It is _____ minutes to _____ .

It is _____ : _____ .

It is _____ minutes to _____ .

It is _____ : _____ .

It is _____ .

It is _____ : _____ .

It is _____ .

It is _____ : _____ .

(3) Tick the time that is the odd one out.

 ☐

 ☐

 ☐

(4) Tick the time that is the odd one out.

 ☐

 ☐

 ☐

Time riddles 1

Use the clues to work out what time it is. Write your answers in digital time.

(1)

Clue A

It is between half past 11 and half past 12.

Clue B

The last two digits are 0 in digital time.

Clue C

The big hand and the small hand both point to the same number.

It is _____.

(2)

Clue A

It is between 5 o'clock and 8 o'clock.

Clue B

The big hand has gone halfway around the clock.

Clue C

The small hand has passed 6 but has not yet passed 7.

It is _____.

(3)

Clue A

It is between 3:00 and 5:00.

Clue B

The hour is a multiple of 2.

Clue C

The big hand is pointing to the number 5.

It is _____.

Lengths of time 1

1 Look at each pair of clocks below.
How much time has passed between the first and second clock?

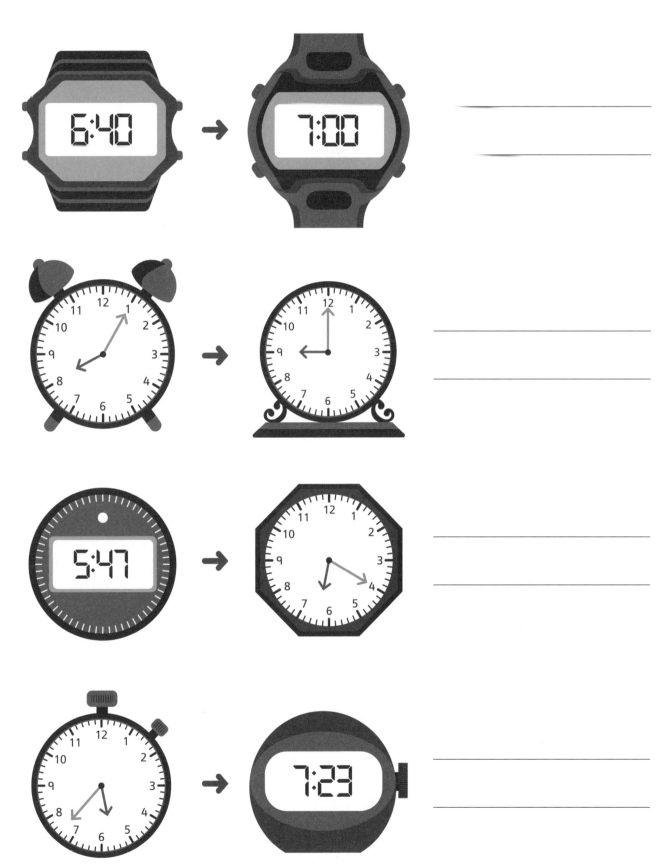

Converting between units of time

Short lengths of time can be measured in **seconds**, **minutes** and **hours**.

There are **60 seconds** in a **minute**.

There are **60 minutes** in an **hour**.

There are **24 hours** in a **day**.

(1) Answer these questions.

Hours and minutes

How many minutes are there in 2 hours? _____ minutes

How many hours do 90 minutes make? _____ hours

Hours and days

How many hours are there in 3 days? _____ hours

How many days do 48 hours make? _____ days

Seconds and minutes

How many seconds are there in 3 minutes? _____ seconds

How many minutes do 120 seconds make? _____ minutes

(2) Write these lengths of time in order from shortest to longest.

80 seconds	1 minute	23 hours	37 minutes

short | | | | | long

50 seconds	27 minutes	1 day	18 hours

short | | | | | long

Did you know?

The earth's rotation is slowing down very slowly, so a day gets longer by 1.7 milliseconds every 100 years. There are 1000 milliseconds in a second.

Converting between units of time

Longer lengths of time can be measured in **days, weeks, months** and **years**.

There are **7 days** in a **week**.

There are **52 weeks** in a **year**.

There are **12 months** in a **year**.

3 Answer these questions.

Months and years

How many months are there in 2 years? _____ months

How many years do 36 months make? _____ years

Weeks and years

How many weeks are there in 2 years? _____ weeks

How many years do 156 weeks make? _____ years

Days and weeks

How many days are there in 3 weeks? _____ days

How many weeks do 35 days make? _____ weeks

4 Draw a line to join these lengths of time in order from shortest to longest.

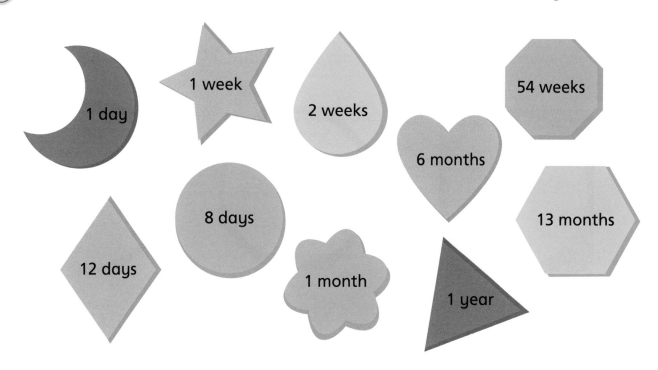

Time fractions

You already know what halves and quarters look like on a clock.

half an hour

$\frac{1}{2}$ hour

quarter of an hour

$\frac{1}{4}$ hour

You can also find other fractions on a clock.

This clock face is divided into thirds.
$\frac{1}{3}$ of an hour is 20 minutes.

There are 60 minutes in an hour, so $\frac{1}{60}$ of an hour is 1 minute.

(1) Colour in these clocks to show the correct fractions. How many minutes are in each fraction?

$\frac{1}{2}$ hour

_____ minutes

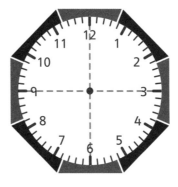

$\frac{1}{4}$ hour

_____ minutes

$\frac{1}{3}$ hour

_____ minutes

Time fractions

2 Draw lines to match each fraction to the correct clock face.

$\frac{3}{4}$ hour $\frac{1}{60}$ hour $\frac{2}{3}$ hour

3 Write the correct fraction of an hour below each clock.

30 minutes   5 minutes   10 minutes

_____ hour   _____ hour   _____ hour

4 Colour in these clocks to show the correct fractions. How many minutes are in each fraction?

$\frac{2}{3}$ hour $\frac{3}{6}$ hour $\frac{4}{12}$ hour

  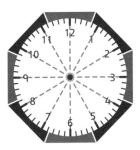

_____ minutes   _____ minutes   _____ minutes

Did you know?

The word 'fraction' comes from the Latin word 'fractio', which means 'breaking'.

Time problems

Learn

Many time problems can be solved by counting on.

Question: Harry's party started at 3 o'clock and lasted for 4 hours. What time did it end?

Method: Count on 4 hours from 3 o'clock.

Answer: 7 o'clock.

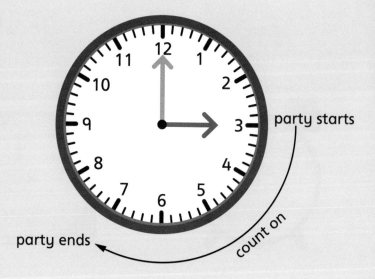

party starts

party ends

count on

Answer these time problems.

1 The film started at 5 o'clock and lasted 2 hours.

What time did it end?

_____

2 The painters worked until 12 o'clock and then took a lunch break for an hour.

What time did they finish lunch?

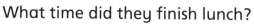

_____

3 A pie went into the oven at half past 4. It baked for 45 minutes.

What time was it ready?

_____

4 Gita began reading a book at 3:00 and read for 1 and a half hours.

What time did she stop reading?

_____

5 Zain got on the tram at ten minutes past 9. He got off at half past 9.

How long did his journey last?

_____

6 A TV programme started at 3:25 and lasted for half an hour.

What time did it finish?

_____

22

Time problems

For more difficult problems, you can draw a **number line** to help you.

Question: Tom got on the train at 1:15 and got off at 3:30. How long was his journey?

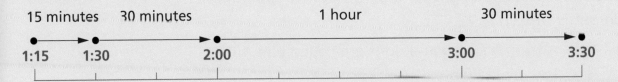

15 minutes	30 minutes		1 hour		30 minutes
1:15	1:30	2:00		3:00	3:30

Method: 15 minutes + 30 minutes + 1 hour + 30 minutes = 2 hours 15 minutes

Answer: 2 hours and 15 minutes

Answer these time problems.

---

(7) Amirah's piano lesson started at 4:45 and ended at 6:00.

How long was her lesson?

_____

---

(8) A helicopter took off at quarter past 10 and landed at 20 minutes past 12.

How long was the journey?

_____

---

(9) Dad went shopping at 2:10. He got home at 5:35.

How long was he out?

_____

---

(10) Oliver took his new puppy for a walk for 50 minutes. He left at 10:35.

What time did he get back?

_____

---

(11) Mum went to the hairdresser at 4:55. She got back 1 hour and 10 minutes later. What time did she get back?

_____

---

(12) A doctor has 10 minutes to see each patient. She starts her day at 8:30. How many patients can she see before 12:30?

_____

The 12-hour clock

Learn

There are 24 hours in a day. The small hand takes 12 hours to go all the way around an analogue clock. It does this twice in a day. This is called the **12-hour clock**.

The 12 hours from midnight to noon are called **a.m.** times.
Midnight is written as 12:00 a.m.

The 12 hours from noon to midnight are called **p.m.** times.
Noon is written as 12:00 p.m.

12-hour clock

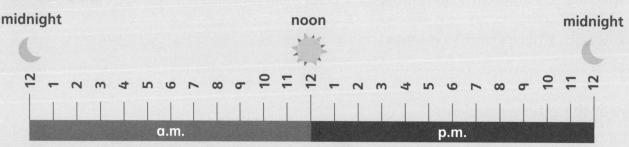

Remember – if you just write '2 o'clock' by itself, you could mean 2 o'clock in the afternoon or 2 o'clock in the morning! But if you write '2:00 p.m.', it is clear that you mean the afternoon.

---

1 Tick the correct time for each picture.

☐ 7:00 a.m.	
☐ 7:00 p.m.	

☐ 11:00 a.m.	
☐ 11:00 p.m.	

☐ 3:00 a.m.	
☐ 3:00 p.m.	

☐ 1:00 a.m.	
☐ 1:00 p.m.	

Did you know?

a.m. stands for 'ante meridian', which is Latin for 'before noon'.
p.m. stands for 'post meridian', which is Latin for 'after noon'.

The 12-hour clock

(2) Write **a.m.** or **p.m.** to complete each sentence.

The sun rises at 5:15 _____ .

The sun sets at 5:50 _____ .

Sam goes to bed at 8:00 _____ .

Sam wakes up at 6:30 _____ .

I eat supper at 7:00 _____ .

I eat lunch at 12:00 _____ .

(3) Tick the clock that shows the latest time.

(4) Tick the clock that shows the earliest time.

The 24-hour clock

You already know how to write digital time using the 12-hour clock.

12-hour clock

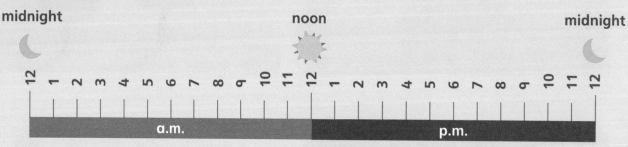

There is another way of writing digital time, instead of using a.m. and p.m. This is called the **24-hour clock**.

24-hour clock

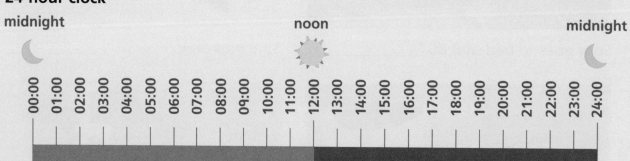

The a.m. hours (before noon) are written as 01:00, 02:00 and so on until noon, which is 12:00. Then the p.m. hours carry on from 12. So 1:00 p.m. is written as 13:00 and 2:00 p.m. as 14:00 and so on until midnight, which is 00:00.

To change p.m. times to 24-hour times, you add on 12 hours.

Example: 3:00 p.m. = 3 + 12 hours = 15:00

---

(1) Write these times in 24-hour time.

2 a.m.   = [: 00]   5:30 a.m. = [:   ]   Midnight = [:   ]

2 p.m.   = [: 00]   5:30 p.m. = [:   ]   Noon = [:   ]

The Ancient Egyptians were the first people to divide a day into 24 hours. They based this on the movement of shadows during the day and the movement of stars at night.

The 24-hour clock

2 Draw lines to show if these 24-hour times are before or after noon.

 a.m.   p.m.

04:00   20:35   13:50   10:45

3 Draw lines to match the clocks that show the same time.

4 Tick the clock that shows the latest time.

5 Tick the clock that shows the earliest time.

Time riddles 2

Use the clues to work out what time it is. Write your answers in 24-hour time.

1

Clue A

In 24-hour time the hour is a multiple of 5.

Clue B

In 24-hour time the hour is greater than 16.

Clue C

There is 1 minute to go before the next hour.

It is _____.

2

Clue A

In 24-hour time the hour is less than 1.

Clue B

In 24-hour time the last digit is 5.

Clue C

In 15 minutes it will be 10 minutes past the next hour.

It is _____.

3

Clue A

In 24-hour time the hour is a multiple of 10.

Clue B

In 12-hour time it is an a.m. time.

Clue C

On an analogue clock the big hand points to 4.

It is _____.

Lengths of time 2

1 Look at each pair of clocks below.
How much time has passed between the first and second clock?

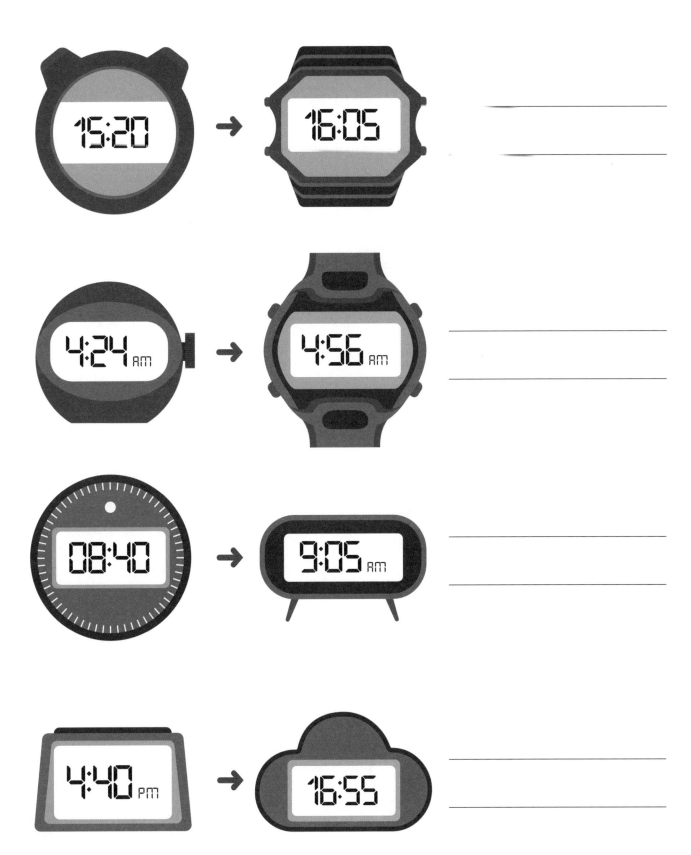

Time problems using the 24-hour clock

Answer these time problems. Write your answers in 24-hour time.

1 A bus leaves Reading at 13:50 and arrives in London at 16:00.

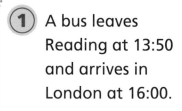

How long is the journey?

_____

2 A flight from Germany to France takes 2 hours. An aeroplane leaves Germany at 11:05.

What time does it land in France?

_____

3 It takes Krishna 46 minutes to cycle to work.

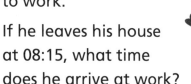

If he leaves his house at 08:15, what time does he arrive at work?

_____

4 Annie puts cupcakes in the oven at 12:45. They take 20 minutes to bake, 10 minutes to cool and 10 minutes to decorate.

What time will the cupcakes be ready?

_____

5 A family starts eating in a restaurant at 18:00. The starter takes 20 minutes, the main course takes 30 minutes and the dessert takes 15 minutes.

What time do they finish eating dessert?

_____

6 Jess is going to a play that starts at 19:25. It will take her 25 minutes to get to the theatre and she wants to arrive 10 minutes early to collect her ticket.

What time should she set off from home?

_____

7 A tennis match starts at 16:20. It ends at 17:30.

How long is the match?

_____

8 The bus from Slough to Windsor Castle takes 20 minutes.

If the bus leaves Slough at 11:05, what time does it arrive at the castle?

_____

Schofield & Sims Telling the Time 3

Timetables

When you are travelling by bus or train, you can check a **timetable** to see what time your transport will depart and arrive.

Timetables often use the 24-hour clock.

1 Look at the timetable and answer the questions below.

Station	Train 1	Train 2	Train 3	Train 4
Amberton	07:30	08:45	10:00	11:30
Bostown	07:45	09:00	10:15	11:45
Calthorpe	08:55	10:10	11:35	12:07
Denton	09:10	10:25	11:50	12:25
Farmore	09:55	11:05	12:30	13:15
Gatstone	10:25	11:35	13:00	13:45

What time does the 07:30 from Amberton get to Calthorpe? _____

How long is the journey from Denton to Gatstone on Train 2? _____

Which train takes the longest to get from Amberton to Gatstone? _____

How long does it take for the train that
leaves Amberton at 08:45 to get to Farmore? _____

If you arrive at Bostown station at 10:55, how long
will you have to wait until the next train for Denton? _____

If you need to arrive at Gatstone by noon,
which train should you catch from Amberton? _____

Jamie lives in Bostown and has a flute lesson in Calthorpe
at 12:00. Should he aim to catch Train 3 or Train 4? _____

Did you know?

Some high-speed trains can reach speeds of over 300 miles per hour.

Roman numerals

The numbers you use and write every day are called **Arabic numerals**.
The Romans had their own set of numbers called **Roman numerals**.
Some clock faces have Roman numerals instead of the usual numbers 1 to 12.

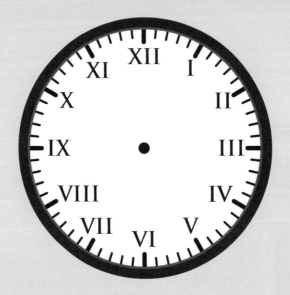

For 1, 2 and 3 the Romans used **I**, **II** and **III**.
For 5 and 10 they used **V** and **X**.

4 was 1 <u>less</u> than 5, so it was **IV**.

6 was 1 <u>more</u> than 5, so it was **VI**.
7 was 2 <u>more</u> than 5, so it was **VII**.
8 was 3 <u>more</u> than 5, so it was **VIII**.

9 was 1 <u>less</u> than 10, so it was **IX**.

11 was 1 <u>more</u> than 10, so it was **XI**.
12 was 2 <u>more</u> than 10, so it was **XII**.

(1) Write the missing Roman numerals in the table.

1	2	3	4	5	6	7	8	9	10	11	12
I			IV	V			VIII			XI	

(2) Solve the calculations. Give your answers in Roman numerals.

VIII – V = ⬚   IV + I = ⬚   XI – II = ⬚

Roman numerals

3 What time is it?

It is _____ .

It is _____ .

It is _____ .

It is _____ .

It is _____ .

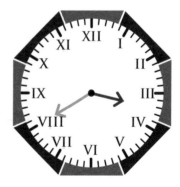

It is _____ .

Did you know?

The Romans also had numerals for larger numbers: **L** for 50, **C** for 100, **D** for 500, **M** for 1000.

Time zones

As the earth spins on its axis, the sun only shines on one part of the planet. For example, when the morning sun is shining in the United Kingdom, it is night-time in North America.

Because of these time differences, the world is divided into **time zones**. All the places within each stripe on this map have the same time.

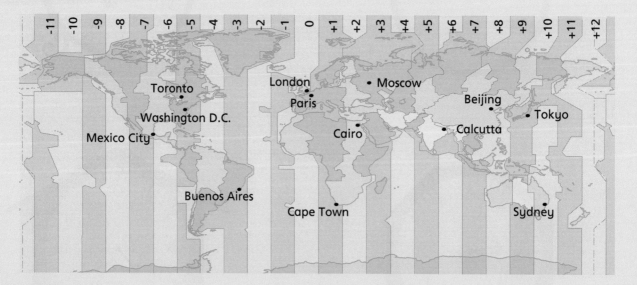

When you go abroad, you often have to change your watch to a different time. Some countries are so wide that there are several time zones within them.

(1) Help the holiday-makers put their clocks forward or back.

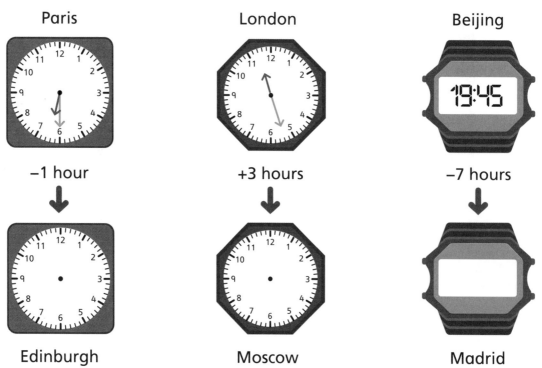

Paris	London	Beijing
−1 hour	+3 hours	−7 hours
Edinburgh	Moscow	Madrid

Time-zone problems

If you travel around the world, you will eventually reach a place where the time is either one day ahead or one day behind. The **International Date Line** is the imaginary line on the earth's surface that you cross when this happens.

Answer these time problems. Write your answers in 24-hour time.

1 Paris in France is 1 hour ahead of London.
What time is it in Paris when it is 10:00 in London?

_____

2 Lisbon in Portugal is in the same time zone as London.
What time is it in Lisbon when it is 19:00 in London?

_____

3 Beijing in China is 8 hours ahead of London.
What time is it in London when it is 05:00 in Beijing?

_____

4 Moscow in Russia is 3 hours ahead of London.
What time is it in Moscow when it is 12:30 in London?

_____

5 New York in the USA is 5 hours behind London.
What time is it in London when it is 23:00 on a Tuesday in New York? What day of the week is it?

_____

_____

6 Canberra in Australia is 11 hours ahead of London.
What time is it in Canberra when it is 18:30 on a Monday in London? What day of the week is it?

_____

_____

The sun appears to move from east to west because the earth spins from west to east. Try shining a torch on a spinning globe to see this effect.

Daylight Saving Time

Learn

Many countries adjust their time to create an extra hour of daylight in the evening, so it gets dark later in the summer months.

In spring, the clocks are put <u>forward</u> an hour overnight, changing from 1:00 a.m. to 2:00 a.m. On the night the clocks change you lose an hour of sleep.

In autumn, the clocks are put <u>back</u> an hour overnight, changing from 2:00 a.m. to 1:00 a.m. On the night the clocks change you get an extra hour of sleep.

1 **Forward** or **back**? Write the correct word in these sentences.

In spring, the clocks go _____ to Daylight Saving Time.

In autumn, the clocks go _____ to Standard Time.

2 It is spring and the clocks need changing to Daylight Saving Time. Draw the hands on the clock to show the correct time.

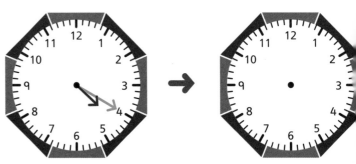

3 It is autumn and the clocks need changing to Standard Time. Draw the hands on the clock to show the correct time.

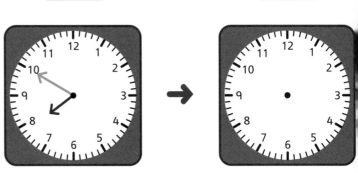

4 It is spring. Laura goes to bed at 22:00 every night. Every morning she gets up to go to work at 06:00. Tonight the clocks are changing to Daylight Saving Time.

How many hours of sleep does Laura usually get? _____ hours

On the night the clocks change, how many hours of sleep will she get? _____ hours

Did you know?

The American politician and writer Benjamin Franklin first came up with the idea of adjusting time in 1784. He suggested that if people started and finished their day earlier they would save on candles in the evening.

Schofield & Sims Telling the Time 3

Answers

Page 4

31, 28 or 29 in a leap year, 31, 30, 31, 30, 31, 31, 30, 31, 30, 31

Page 5

a decade, a century, a year

20 years, 50 years, 300 years, 10 decades

Pages 6–7

Thursday, Wednesday, 5, 4, Thursday, Friday, yes (29 days in the month)

Monday, 5, 4, 14th June, Tuesday, 2 weeks

Page 8

10 minutes past 9, 20 minutes past 12, quarter past 3/15 minutes past 3, 5 minutes past 11

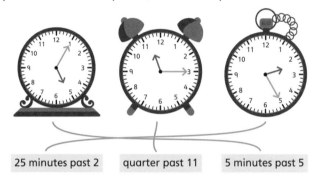

| 25 minutes past 2 | quarter past 11 | 5 minutes past 5 |

Page 9

1 20 minutes to 6, 5 minutes to 3, 10 minutes to 12, quarter to 4/15 minutes to 4

2

Pages 10–11

1 5 minutes past 7, 25 minutes past 8, 5 minutes to 10

2

3

4

Pages 12–13

1 7 minutes past 10

2 17 minutes past 2, 2:17; 26 minutes past 3, 3:26; 11 minutes past 4, 4:11; 23 minutes past 8, 8:23

3

4

Pages 14–15

1 12 minutes to 6

2 6 minutes to 8, 7:54; 11 minutes to 5, 4:49; 2 minutes to 6, 5:58; 27 minutes to 1, 12:33

3

4

Page 16

1 12:00

2 6:30

3 4:25

Answers

Page 17

1 20 minutes, 55 minutes,
   33 minutes, 1 hour 46 minutes

Pages 18–19

1 120 minutes, $1\frac{1}{2}$ hours, 72 hours, 2 days,
   180 seconds, 2 minutes

2 1 minute, 80 seconds, 37 minutes, 23 hours
   50 seconds, 27 minutes, 18 hours, 1 day

3 24 months, 3 years, 104 weeks, 3 years, 21 days,
   5 weeks

4 1 day, 1 week, 8 days, 12 days, 2 weeks, 1 month,
   6 months, 1 year, 54 weeks, 13 months

Pages 20–21

1

30 minutes
(either half shaded)

15 minutes
(any quarter shaded)

20 minutes
(any third shaded)

2
$\frac{3}{4}$ hour $\frac{1}{60}$ hour $\frac{2}{3}$ hour

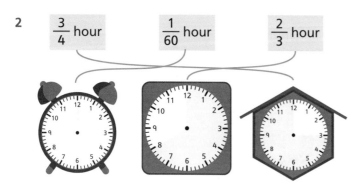

3 $\frac{1}{2}$ hour, $\frac{1}{12}$ hour, $\frac{1}{6}$ hour

4

40 minutes
(any two thirds shaded)

30 minutes
(any three sixths shaded)

20 minutes
(any four twelfths shaded)

Pages 22–23

1 7 o'clock/7:00

2 1 o'clock/1:00

3 quarter past 5/fifteen minutes past 5/5:15

4 4:30/half past 4

5 20 minutes

6 3:55/5 minutes to 4

7 1 hour 15 minutes

8 2 hours 5 minutes

9 3 hours 25 minutes

10 11:25/25 minutes past 11

11 6:05/5 minutes past 6

12 24

Pages 24–25

1 7:00 a.m., 11:00 p.m., 3:00 p.m., 1:00 p.m.

2 a.m., p.m., p.m., a.m., p.m., p.m.

3

4

Pages 26–27

1 02:00, 14:00; 05:30, 17:30; 00:00, 12:00

Answers

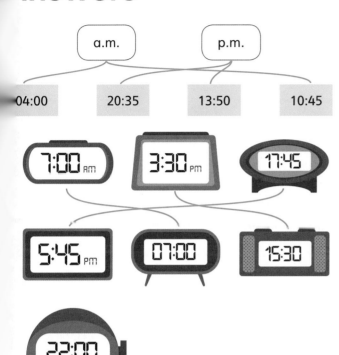

Page 28

1 20:59

2 00:55

3 10:20

Page 29

1 45 minutes, 32 minutes, 25 minutes, 15 minutes

Page 30

1 2 hours 10 minutes

2 13:05

3 09:01

4 13:25

5 19:05

6 18:50

7 1 hour 10 minutes

8 11:25

Page 31

1 08:55,1 hour 10 minutes, Train 3
2 hours 20 minutes, 50 minutes, 08:45/Train 2,
Train 3

Pages 32–33

1 II, III, VI, VII, IX, X, XII

2 III, V, IX

3 10 o'clock/10:00, 10 minutes past 5/5:10, quarter
past 9/15 minutes past 9/9:15, 25 minutes past 7
/7:25, quarter to 3/15 minutes to 3/2:45, 20 minutes
to 4/3:40

Page 34

1

Page 35

1 11:00

2 19:00

3 21:00

4 15:30

5 04:00, Wednesday

6 05:30, Tuesday

Page 36

1 forward, back

2

3

4 8 hours, 7 hours

Schofield&Sims

the long-established educational publisher specialising in maths, English and science

Telling the time is a vital life skill. **Schofield & Sims Telling the Time** breaks this difficult topic down into a sequence of manageable ideas that young learners can approach at their own pace. Beginning with child-friendly explanations of times of day and units of time, the series moves on to introduce telling the time on an analogue clock, before progressing to cover a wide range of related concepts, including different ways of measuring and representing time, time expressions and everyday time problems.

Each activity book provides:

- large, clear clock faces for easy counting
- colour-coded hands to aid recognition of hours and minutes
- 'Learn' panels that explain time-telling in simple steps
- fun general-knowledge facts to enrich learning
- targeted practice, including counting activities, matching exercises, and drawing the hands on the clock
- answers to all the practice questions in the book.

Telling the Time 3 meets all the National Curriculum time requirements for Years 3 and 4. It covers reading and writing the time to the nearest minute; converting between analogue and digital 12- and 24-hour clocks; comparing durations of events; Roman numerals; timetables; time zones; and problem-solving involving converting between units of time (including seconds, minutes, hours, days, weeks, months and years).

Telling the Time 1   ISBN 978 07217 1418 9
Telling the Time 2   ISBN 978 07217 1419 6
Telling the Time 3   ISBN 978 07217 1420 2

Have you tried **Times Tables Practice** by Schofield & Sims?

This series of books gives children extensive practice in all the times tables relevant to their age group, providing enjoyable activities with attractive illustrations that will hold their attention throughout.

ISBN 978-07217-1420-2

9 780721 714202 >

MIX
Paper from responsible sources
FSC www.fsc.org FSC® C023114

ISBN 978 07217 1420 2
Key Stage 2
Age range 7–9 years

£3.50 (Retail price)

For further information and to place your order visit
www.schofieldandsims.co.uk or telephone 01484 607080

Schofield&Sims

Telling the Time 3

Name

Note for teachers and parents

Learning to tell the time is a complex process that many children need help to grasp. This series breaks down telling the time into very small steps that every child can understand. Featuring clear step-by-step learning, varied practice activities and fun time facts, these workbooks provide everything children need to master this essential life skill.

Telling the Time 3 revises the basics of telling the time before introducing the 12-hour clock, the 24-hour clock and clocks with Roman numerals. The children also encounter problem-solving challenges that explore time in relation to fractions, converting between units of time, and reading calendars and timetables. This book supports the National Curriculum for Mathematics at Lower Key Stage 2, but it can also be used with older children who require additional support.

Try to discuss time as often as you can with the child and draw attention to different means of time-telling such as a clock on the wall, a wristwatch or time displays on phones and computers. Questions such as "What time do you go to sleep?" and "How long does it take to get to school?" will help the child to think about the importance of time measurement and to become familiar with vocabulary that relates to time.

Each book features large clock faces that young fingers can easily count on. When introducing each new time, encourage the child to count aloud and point to the numbers around the edge of the clock. This will help to secure the idea that the hands of the clock are constantly moving around the circle of the clock face. The hands of the clock are colour-coded throughout the series – blue for the minute hand and red for the hour hand – to help the child to identify them quickly.

Children are given frequent opportunities to practise their learning through a variety of activities, such as drawing the hands on the clock, matching activities, riddles, and word and number problems. You will find answers to all the activities at the back of the book.

Published by **Schofield & Sims Ltd**, Dogley Mill, Fenay Bridge, Huddersfield HD8 0NQ, UK
Telephone 01484 607080
www.schofieldandsims.co.uk

This edition copyright © Schofield & Sims Ltd, 2017
First published in 2017

Author: **Christine Shaw**
Christine Shaw has asserted her moral rights under the Copyright, Designs and Patents Act, 1988, to be identified as the author of this work.

British Library Cataloguing in Publication Data
A catalogue record for this book is available from the British Library.

Design by **Oxford Designers & Illustrators Ltd**

Printed in the UK by **Page Bros (Norwich) Ltd**

ISBN 978 07217 1420 2